Three hunters were returning home one evening. As they got close to their village, a rabbit jumped out from the hedge and into the middle of the track. It sat and looked at them. The hunters quickly raised their bows and shot at the rabbit. But all of the arrows missed.

They blinked in amazement. Then suddenly, instead of a rabbit, there stood an old man.

“Please,” he begged, “I’m sick and in need of help.”

The hunters shook their heads and continued on.

“We are hunters, and we are tired and on our way home,” they said as they walked on by.

The hunters soon vanished along the track. The old man followed slowly behind them. In a little while, he reached the village. He stopped and looked around. There were several lodges in a circle. He headed to the first lodge.

He stopped and spoke to the elder sitting outside the lodge.

"Please can you help? I am sick."

"Go away," the elder said rudely. "We don't wish any sickness in our clan."

The old man shuffled along to the Beaver Lodge, "Please can you help me?"

"No," replied the young man, "we have no food to share. Go away."

The old man looked to where the hunters stood with all the things they had caught. He shook his head sadly.

He shuffled along and in turn he tried the Deer Lodge and the Turtle Lodge. They too shook their heads and sent him on his way, saying they couldn't help.

Next he tried the Hawk, Snipe, and Heron lodges, which were a bit further along on the edge of the forest. By now it was getting darker and also colder. The old man started to shiver.

At the very far end of the village, next to the river, was the Bear Lodge. The old man approached it. The Bear Clan's mother took one look at the old man and greeted him, saying, "Come in. You look like you need some rest and care." She lifted the blanket that covered the doorway, and beckoned the old man inside.

Inside the lodge, she found the old man a seat by the fire and gave him a dish of freshly made cornmeal porridge. He ate the food gratefully. Then the Bear Clan mother wrapped him in some soft skins and the old man quickly fell asleep.

The following morning, the old man awoke but he was no better. When the Bear Clan mother checked on him, he told her she needed to collect some herbs from the woods. She collected the herbs and prepared them as he told her. The old man took the medicine. The following morning he was much better. Within a few days he was completely better.

Despite feeling better, the old man stayed with the Bear Clan. A few days later, he was ill again. Again the Bear Clan mother cared for him and listened when he told her to collect some roots and leaves to make the medicine he needed. Once he had taken the medicine, he again recovered quickly.

The old man remained with the Bear Clan, and every few weeks he would fall sick with a different illness: a fever, a pain, a rash, or a cold. Each time he fell ill, he would instruct the Bear Clan mother as to what to do, how to make the different medicines and how to treat him. The Bear Clan mother listened carefully and remembered everything he told her.

Soon, she knew more than anyone else about illnesses, how to make medicines, and how to make everyone better.

One evening, the Bear Clan mother and the old man were sitting outside the lodge, gazing up at all of the stars in the sky. The old man turned to Bear Clan mother and explained, “I was sent by the great spirit to teach all of his children the secrets of healing. However, you and your clan are the only ones who welcomed me and cared for me.”

“You are the only ones who know how to heal the sick and make medicines. From now on, all of the other clans will have to come to you to learn how to heal. The Bear Clan will be strong because of this.”

The Bear Clan mother was very happy. She looked up to the stars, and thanked the great spirit for his gift.

When she had finished, she turned to the old man again, but he had gone. She was sitting alone, under the stars and all she could see was a plump little rabbit hopping away into the distance.